Handbooks of UK Wastewater Practice

PRELIMINARY PROCESSES

Third Edition

The Institution of Water
and Environmental Management

© The Institute of
Water Pollution Control 1972, 1984
© The Institution of
Water and Environmental Management 1992

ISBN 1 870752 14 7

First published 1972
Revised 1984
Third edition 1992

The Institution of
Water and Environmental Management
15 John Street, London WC1N 2EB

CONTENTS

FIGURES

PLATES

ACKNOWLEDGEMENTS

The Institution gratefully acknowledges permission from the following to reproduce figures and plates.

Biwater Engineering Ltd, Heywood.	Fig. 8, and Plate 2
Bord Na Mona, Co. Kildare, Ireland.	Fig. 2
C & H Waste Processing, Yeovil.	Fig. 12
Detectronic Ltd, Blackburn.	Fig. 21
Dorr Oliver Co Ltd, Croydon.	Figs. 7 & 14
Energy and Waste Systems Ltd, Westbury.	Fig. 6
Hydro Research and Development Ltd, Bristol.	Fig. 16
Jones and Attwood, Ltd, Stourbridge.	Figs. 9 & 15, and Plate 1
Longwood Engineering Ltd, Huddersfield.	Figs. 4 & 10
Ozotech Ltd, Burgess Hill.	Fig. 1
Strathclyde Regional Council.	Frontispiece
Thames Water Utilities, Reading.	Plate 3
Vickerys Ltd, Greenwich.	Fig. 5
Waste-Tec Dresser, Stockport	Fig. 11
Watson Hawksley, High Wycombe.	Fig. 13
Yorkshire Water Services Ltd, Leeds.	Plates 4 & 5

FOREWORD

The Institution of Water and Environmental Management (IWEM) is a corporate learned society and examining body representing the interests of engineers and scientists and other professionally qualified personnel working in the various sectors of the environment: water, air and land. It was formed in July 1987 by the unification of three eminent organizations, The Institution of Public Health Engineers, The Institution of Water Engineers and Scientists, and The Institute of Water Pollution Control, each having a history of some 100 years.

Over the years the predecessor bodies have produced definitive manuals and other publications, notably in respect of British practice in the water industry. These have become reference sources for those who are actively engaged in the field, as well as for students seeking authoritative guidance in preparing for professional qualifications. Such publications are being continued by IWEM, and the range is being extended to take account of the wider environmental interests which the new organization embraces.

The Handbook *Preliminary Processes* was the first in a series to be produced by the former Institute of Water Pollution Control in 1972, and it was reprinted with amendments in 1984. Since then there have been major developments in fine screening, and new sections are included to cover these. There are also new sections on septicity, odour control and flow balancing, and the text has been revised to accommodate many other changes.

The Handbook has been revised by Nick Sambidge, and the Institution wishes to record its thanks to him and to those members and suppliers of equipment who have contributed.

H.D.M. Speed
President

November 1992

1. Introduction

1.1 Purpose of Preliminary Treatment

Sewage contains polluting matter in many forms. In addition to dissolved impurities it contains material in suspension and in colloidal form which can be broadly divided into organic and inorganic material. The size of the particles of suspended matter also varies widely.

Gross solids and grit can cause blockages, damage and wear to pipework, valves, pumps and treatment equipment. The aim of preliminary treatment is to protect subsequent treatment processes.

A research project on the problems caused by screenings and grit in sewage was undertaken by the Construction Industry Research and Information Association (CIRIA) in conjunction with the Water Research Centre (WRc) and reports were published in 1984, 1985 and 1988[1,2,3]. They identified many shortcomings in the equipment commonly in use. From this there developed a project, carried out together by Welsh Water (WW) and WRc, on sea outfall headworks, which examined the equipment available to meet rising environmental standards. Since the mid-1980s there has been a rapid advance in the technology of sewage screening, with the emphasis on fine and milli-screens.

Although preliminary treatment will be discussed with particular reference to sewage treatment, many of the types of equipment mentioned are widely used in the pre-treatment of industrial effluents at factory sites prior to their discharge to foul sewer or to watercourse.

At small sewage treatment works serving populations up to 1000 persons, screening and grit removal are frequently omitted, and debris allowed to collect in the settlement tank. Where power is available, a disintegrator is often installed to break up solid matter to avoid blockages in sludge pipelines, distributors, and dosing siphons. Provision should also be made for measuring and recording the sewage flow, and at small works a weir near the outlet is usually a requirement of the National Rivers Authority (NRA).

1.2 Septicity

Domestic sewage contains sulphur compounds, and effluents from the leather, brewing and paper industries can contain very high levels. Bacterial activity quickly depletes any dissolved oxygen which is present and septicity can easily develop. Under anaerobic conditions organic sulphur compounds and sulphates are reduced to form sulphides, mercaptans and skatole; and other reactions result in the formation of aldehydes, amines, fatty acids and indole. The principle product, hydrogen sulphide, is formed mainly in the slime which grows on the wall of the sewer. The most favourable conditions for its production are a small diameter pipe with a large internal surface area per unit volume, filled with anaerobic sewage for a long period, at a high ambient temperature.

Hydrogen sulphide can contaminate the atmosphere in manholes, gravity sewers, and wet wells of pumping stations. It is a flammable and very poisonous gas with the characteristic odour of rotten eggs, and when escaping into the atmosphere it can cause serious odour nuisance. It is particularly dangerous to workers in sewers because the capability to smell the gas diminishes with exposure and as the concentration increases. It is acutely toxic to aquatic organisms, and could be a factor in fish kills near storm sewage overflows. Hydrogen sulphide in damp conditions can damage concrete, electrical equipment, step-irons and ladders[4]. Where the sewage flow is turbulent, hydrogen sulphide escapes into the air space, and, in the damp warm atmosphere, can be oxidized to sulphuric acid by autotrophic thiobacilli which grow on exposed walls. The resultant corrosion effect that follows is most noticeable at or above the water line of sewers, and in wet wells and manholes. Pumping mains after a period of no flow, e.g. overnight, will often discharge large amounts of hydrogen sulphide into a wet well, manhole or gravity sewer leading to both odour complaints and corrosion.

At a sewage works there is also potential for septicity when the sewage is held for some hours in the primary settlement tanks, particularly when they are not desludged frequently. Desludging is best achieved using automatic equipment. Sludge undergoing treatment can be septic, and treatment and disposal operations have to be designed and operated in such a way as to minimize any nuisance. All sewage treatment works have a background odour, but at most works where the sewage is fresh those odours that do occur are usually local, short-lived and not generally offensive. However, they may linger on still days or during periods of temperature inversion. Odour nuisance leads to strong reaction from local residents, and the Environmental Health Department of the Local Authority has power to serve an abatement notice, or it can prosecute in more serious cases. Action to prevent the formation of toxic conditions in the sewer, corrosion, and odour nuisance, is usually based on either maintaining aerobic conditions by adding oxygen in some form, or inhibiting bacterial activity with chlorine. A symposium[5] organised in 1979 by the Institute of Water Pollution Control (IWPC) provided a good review of the subject.

The formation of hydrogen sulphide can be prevented by maintaining a dissolved oxygen concentration greater than 0.2 mg/l in the sewage. Oxygen may be added in a rising main, where, in addition to preventing septicity, it can reduce the biochemical oxygen demand (BOD) of the sewage before it arrives at the sewage works[6]. It is normally supplied as compressed gas in cylinders and passed through a vaporizer to a fine nozzle located in the rising main close to the outlet from the pump. The system is simple to install and operate, and requires little attention.

Hydrogen peroxide, used as a 35% w/w solution, is a stable, non-corrosive and easily handled liquid source of oxygen. A dosing system is easy and cheap to install, needing only a storage tank, metering pump and injection point in the rising main or wet well. In the absence of dissolved oxygen, nitrate can be a source of oxygen for bacteria to prevent the onset of septic conditions. Proprietary chemical formulations are available containing nitrate and iron salts; sulphide is precipitated and the nitrate oxygen is utilized by bacteria. These are generally added at the wet well.

1.3 Odour Control

The measurement of odour is a very subjective and inexact art because it has to depend on the personal judgement of ordinary people. In the mid-1970s Warren Spring Laboratory carried out a research programme for the Department of the Environment (DoE), to develop techniques of measurement and analysis of odours. From this came the Dynamic Dilution Apparatus[5] which measures the intensity of an odour. It dilutes the odour with clean air until it can no longer be detected by a panel of four people. The apparatus was used to study odours at sewage works, and very wide variations were recorded. For example inlet works had dilution factors between 500 and 1300, balancing tanks 3000 to 3700, and sludge pumping wells factors of over 300 000.

The removal of the cause of the odour is not always possible and the best solution depends on malodorous air being contained and then treated, but this is not always practical at sewage works. However, buildings and tanks at sewage works are increasingly being designed to allow malodorous air to be extracted and treated. It is clearly good practice to avoid unnecessary contact with the atmosphere, keeping sewage and sludge in pipes, and avoiding excessive turbulence.

Once the malodours have been contained treatment can be carried out. Toogood published a review of suitable methods in 1990[7]. Chemical destruction can be achieved by oxidation with ozone, potassium permanganate, peracetic acid or sodium hypochlorite, and biological treatment is possible by passing the air through beds of peat or compost. With increasing use of sludge incinerators, malodours can be diverted for combustion in appropriate situations.

1.3.1 Chemical control methods. Ozonized air is produced by passing dried air through a silent high voltage electrical discharge, and then drawn into scrubbing water and sprayed downwards through an inert packing against the upward flow of malodorous air (Fig. 1). The treated air passes through a mist eliminator before being returned to the atmosphere. Ozonizers can also be installed over covered tanks, ozone being passed into the tank.

Malodours can also be removed by passing the air through dry scrubber columns

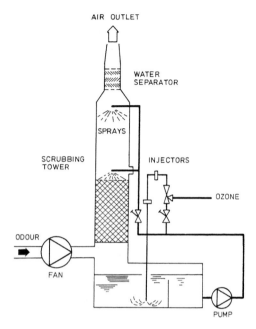

Fig. 1. Wet oxidation with ozone

packed with activated carbon derived from coconut shell, coal or wood. Depending on the grade chosen for the application the structure can provide a surface area of $1000 \ m^2/g$, and odorous compounds are adsorbed onto the surface of the carbon.

Purifill is made up of activated alumina pellets impregnated with potassium permanganate and other reagents. The pellets adsorb hydrogen sulphide onto the surface and in moist conditions it is oxidized. Puracarb medium consists of a mixture of activated carbon and alumina impregnated with sodium bicarbonate to neutralize acid gases, and potassium hydroxide and iodide for control of hydrogen sulphide.

Wet scrubbers are columns packed with loose media down which (usually) caustic final effluent percolates against the upward flow of odorous gas. The effluent is returned to the inlet works for treatment.

Peracetic acid is used mainly as a disinfectant of faecal organisms at sewage outfalls, and also to reduce the activity of sulphide-producing bacteria. However, there is some concern about the decomposition products of this process, and the National Rivers Authority is currently (1992) withholding consent for its use when the discharge is to a watercourse.

1.3.2 Biological control methods. Biological methods using peat and compost beds are finding increasing use for odour destruction at sewage works, and have the

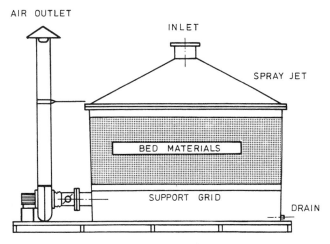

Fig. 2. Peat bed used for odour removal

advantage that they use a process familiar to operators. They utilize moist layers of peat, heather or compost supplied in packaged units. The malodorous air is directed into the base of the bed and rises upwards through the peat; adsorption onto the peat surface allows micro-organisms to degrade the chemicals (Fig. 2). Little attention is needed although the bed should be kept moist.

1.3.3 Odour masking. Odour masking involves mixing the odour with another having a more pleasant smell. It is a short-term solution, attractive because of its low capital cost and speed of installation. The masking chemical is forced by compressed air through atomizers suspended from posts about 4 metres above ground level. This forms a curtain of mist through which smells have to pass. The technique is not always reliable because it depends on achieving the correct balance of masking agent and smell, and on the wind direction. Sometimes the original odour combines with the masking chemical to form another unpleasant odour, or with prolonged use the sewage works operators may complain. A number of different masking agents are available for different applications. The operating costs can be minimized by using a wind vane as a controlling device. The systems are frequently recommended for their ease of installation, particularly around open tanks, but prevention at source is a more positive solution.

2. Flow Balancing

2.1 Introduction

Sewage treatment works operate efficiently when the sewage flow and load arrives continuously and without any short-term variations. Medium-sized and larger works are served by sewerage systems that ensure attenuation of the diurnal peaks. At smaller sewage works close to the centre of population, the sewage arrives at the works more quickly, and can reach the equivalent of 3 times dry weather flow (3 DWF) during the morning and evening peaks with surges as high as 5 to 10 DWF for short periods. These peaks can be accentuated if the village is served by a pumping station, where the minimum pumping rate through the rising main is determined by the velocity needed to avoid settlement. Where several pumping stations deliver to a central works, the flow peaks can be very high especially during rainfall. This may be greater than 3 DWF at a small works and could cause premature storm overflow, and scour solids from the primary and secondary settlement tanks. The average BOD loading to biological treatment may be greatly exceeded during the short period of discharge.

In addition, highly polluting liquors from storm tanks, humus tank desludging or sludge consolidation tanks often drain to a site pumping station, and can be discharged to the inlet works at a very high rate, causing overloading of strength and volume for short periods. The situation may be exacerbated by the emptying of cesspool and septic tank contents into a local sewer, and trade effluents, hotels or schools may have a disproportionate effect. It is not uncommon for sewage works to deal with over half of the daily BOD load during two short periods of the day. In such situations, the quality of effluent discharged to the watercourse can be very variable, and exceed the consent at times.

2.2 Balancing Tanks

Although the balancing of sewage flows has been practised for many years, it has not been given the degree of attention that it warrants, considering the effect that a poor quality sewage effluent can have on the receiving watercourse.

Some degree of balancing can be achieved by ensuring the pumps deliver small amounts at frequent intervals. Recirculation has often been installed specifically to provide dilution and sufficient continuous flow to drive distributors, preventing the biological filters drying out overnight. However, the most common practice adopted has been to make the treatment units larger than necessary for optimum sewage treatment. Hence settlement tanks and filter dosing siphon chambers are commonly able to deal with Formula A flows (see section 5.3). Consequently sewage could become septic in the tanks, and the dosing siphons would operate only infrequently.

The objective of flow balancing is to achieve the level of attenuation that would occur during passage through a larger sewerage system. Flow balancing can also lead to economies in the capacity of treatment units, as well as improved and more reliable treatment.

Incoming sewage is pumped into the balancing tank, and discharged through a flow regulator at a rate which is compatible with the capacity of the treatment units. The size of the balancing tank is determined from the daily flow curve taking account of the height and duration of the peak flow, the outlet rate of discharge and the increase in the water level in the tank.

2.2.1 Flow regulator. Sewage from the balancing tank enters the flow regulator tangentially generating a vortex within the device giving the outlet a high peripheral velocity and an air filled core. The regulator accepts gross sewage solids without blocking, and can be supplied in several sizes to provide a constant and specified rate of discharge from the balancing tank. When sewage enters the balancing tank at a rate much higher than the works can safely accept, the level rises in the tank as the regulator discharges at the predetermined rate. The rate of discharge is approximately constant irrespective of the level in the balancing tank. The common example is the Hydro-Brake flow control used in both balancing tanks and sewerage systems.

2.2.2 Waterbeach. In the 1980s and 90s rapid progress was made in the development of sewage treatment processes for small communities, but the traditional method of balancing was too unreliable and labour-intensive. In 1991 Anglian Water collaborated with WRc to develop the 'Waterbeach'[8] concept of sewage treatment. The aim was to design and build a modular form of sewage treatment works to achieve a consistently high quality effluent. One element of this design was an 'intelligent' balancing tank which linked the essential data to a computer.

The balancing tank is designed on the principle of conversion of flow variations into depth variations within the tank, and the sewage is discharged from the tank by a variable speed pump at a rate of flow compatible with the treatment capacity of the works.

The control system on the balancing tank detects non-typical flows such as during rainfall, and re-adjusts the tank discharge to maximize the use of the balancing tank whilst minimizing the flow changes forward to treatment. The system detects long-term changes and can adjust to seasonal changes in flow. It is also able to deal with frequent fluctuations in flow from small pumping stations.

If the balancing tank fills above a predetermined depth the flow is discharged to a storm tank, and the control system adjusts the flow passing forward to full treatment to the design figure. Stormwater is returned to the balancing tank at a maximum rate of 1 DWF during periods of low influent flow.

The system achieves precise flow balancing, but any load balancing is incidental to the normal operation of the tank.

2.2.3 Floating arm draw-off. Outlets from balancing tanks are frequently constant-flow draw-off floating arms fitted with an orifice plate of appropriate size. A less accurate method involves the use of an orifice plate on the outlet at invert level, and this has the advantage that the tank can be designed to be self-cleansing. Balancing tanks should have an overflow for use in an emergency.

Many of the older balancing tanks were built to combine balancing with screening and grit removal, but in other situations the deposition of debris and grit was to be avoided. Balancing tanks require regular attention to remove rags and fat from the floating arm draw-off, ensure that it has free movement, and empty accumulated grit and sludge.

3. Screening and Disintegration

3.1 Purpose and Choice

Crude sewage contains gross organic and inorganic solids which can damage equipment or create blockages in subsequent treatment plant. In recent years there has been an increase in plastic-based material replacing cellulose-based materials. Traditional screening equipment and disintegrators have not been able to deal with this satisfactorily.

The European Community (EC) Bathing Waters[9] and Dangerous Substances[10] Directives of 1976, and the 1988 Guidelines issued by Her Majesty's Inspectorate of Pollution (HMIP)[11] have been a major force in the developments taking place in the preliminary treatment of sewage at inland works as well as marine headworks for which the Directives were primarily intended.

Screenings may be (a) removed permanently from the flow, (b) removed and then returned after disintegration, or (c) reduced in size by disintegration within the flow.

Until the mid 1980s the traditional type of screen consisted of bars with spaces of 20 to 25 mm. These served the industry very well for over 100 years, but recently fine screens developed from the food industry are increasingly dominating the market. Also during the 1980s, new ranges of more efficient disintegrators began to be installed in large numbers at small sewage works to avoid the need to dispose of debris, and to prevent blockages in filter distributor arms and sludge pipelines.

The choice of screen and aperture size, and choice of disintegrator will depend on the requirements of the sewage and sludge treatment processes. For marine headworks disintegration is no longer feasible because of the requirement to remove all solid matter greater than 6 mm in size, and this is often followed at inland works as well.

3.2 Nature and Quantity of Screenings

The nature of screenings is extremely variable, and detailed information is very limited and unreliable, and should be used with caution. In recent years there has been an increase in the amount of plastic materials which are not so easily removed by traditional screening equipment. As well as interfering with sewage and sludge treatment processes, the application of unscreened sludge to land leads to deposits of unsightly and objectionable debris.

Raw screenings have a foul odour, are objectionable in appearance, and attract vermin. Disposal to Local Authority landfill sites in the untreated state is now less common and screenings may need to be treated before disposal.

The volume of screenings produced depends mainly on the size of the screen aperture as well as the nature and origin of the sewage (Fig. 3). The quantity ranges from 0.01 to 0.03 m^3 per 1000 population, with a density of 600 to 900 kg/m^3 and a moisture content of 80 to 90%. The solids fraction has an organic content of 80 to 90%, and a calorific value of 15×10^3 kJ/kg dry solids. The dry material will normally incinerate but is not autothermic.

3.3 Screening Standards and Design

Until very recently there were no standards by which the design and performance of screens could be judged, and no established techniques for the measurement of performance. The designer relied on the manufacturer's specification and on subjective comment.

Two major studies were carried out between 1982 and 1988 which have added considerably to our knowledge, and from which British Standards are emerging.

The CIRIA/WRc Research Project[1,2,3] led to three reports between 1984 and 1988, dealing with the problems caused by screenings and grit in sewage. It established the scale of the problem and showed that screening and disintegration were very inefficient processes.

In 1986 a WRc Seminar 'Screening and Grit Removal at Sewage Treatment Plants and Sea Outfall Headworks'[12] led to a collaboration between Welsh Water and WRc which examined the efficiency of preliminary processes for marine outfalls, identified appropriate plant, and devised performance tests. A *Users Guide*[13] was produced.

Perhaps not surprisingly it has proved very difficult to devise standards of performance for screens. Doubts have been expressed about the efficiency of the traditional type of screen for some years. In work carried out in 1985, Page[14] established that medium-sized screens captured no more than 50-60% of screenable material. Page further pointed out that most of the remainder is settled in the primary settlement tanks and 0.2% passed forward to the biological stage. The results were based on records of skips emptied and on the solids removed by different sized meshes suspended in the sewage flow. The volume of screenings produced reached very high peaks during a day, and taking 15-minute periods Page found that the peaks were often equivalent to 29 times the average daily rate.

Measurement of the effectiveness of screens was one of the main objectives of the collaborative work by WW/WRc, and the tests, together with the results, are

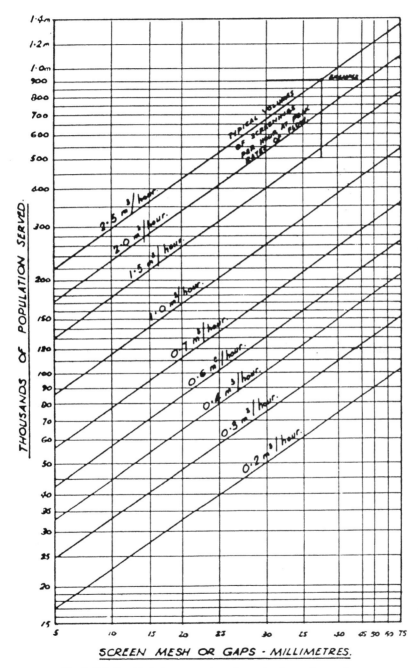

Fig. 3. Relationship between aperture size and volume of screenings

available in the *Users Guide*. A summary of the work as well as a description of the tests, and a recommendation that they be adopted as a general standard, has been presented by Thomas *et al*[15].

The tests briefly comprised:

a) **Plastic Tracer Material**
   Known quantities of labelled plastic items (strips, sticks, condoms) were placed in the sewage flow upstream of the screen and the numbers captured by the screen or passing downstream were recorded.

b) **Mesh Test**
   Aluminium test rigs (0.3 m × 0.3 m) with three wire mesh screens in series 25 mm apart were submerged upstream and downstream of the screen. The mesh sizes of the test screens were 17, 12, and 6 mm respectively, positioned with the coarse screen first.

c) **Hydrodynamic Separator**
   A portable Hydrocyclone was used in which a vortex was created such that the flow spiralled slowly down the inside wall and then up the central axis to overflow. The solid matter dropped out and collected in the bottom, and was then passed through wire meshes to determine the size categories.

d) **Run-down Screen**
   Sewage from a header tank overflowed onto an inclined wedgewire screen with 1 mm apertures. Liquid passed through the screen, and the screenings were collected at the bottom and passed through different sized meshes as above.

e) **Qualitative Coarse Mesh**
   A mesh grid with apertures 50 mm × 30 mm was placed in the discharge channel for two hours, and the amount and type of debris collected gave an indication of the efficiency of the screen.

Sometimes not all the tests were carried out because of restricted access to channels and equipment or because of turbulent flow in the channels. Nevertheless these tests showed how screen performance could be assessed, and variations of (a), (d), and (e) are recommended for a 'Standard Test'.

Several different types of screen have been developed, and to describe them the CIRIA/WRc convention is used:

Coarse screens	>50 mm aperture
Medium	15 to 50 mm
Fine	3 to 15 mm
Milli-screens	0.25 to 3 mm

Mesh net screens such as the Copa-Sac are not strictly a process within Preliminary Treatment, but are described because they provide very effective screening prior to biological filters, and for the final effluent.

The HMIP Guideline[11] requires that all schemes which come within the EC Bathing Water Directive must provide " . . . fine screening or an equally suitable process to remove persistent sewage debris. Adequate performance is unlikely to be achieved by a mesh aperture greater than 6 mm . . . "

In order to satisfy the HMIP Standard for a sea outfall the apertures must be no larger than 6 mm in any direction, and this reduces the choice of screens quite considerably. Designers of inland works tend towards the same standards.

The design of the screen chamber and approach channel is well established, and the following equation is often used for determining the width of the screening chamber:

$$W = \frac{B + S}{S} \times \frac{F}{VD}$$

where W = width of channel in which the screen is fixed (m)
B = width of each screen bar (mm)
S = width of spaces between the bars (mm)
F = maximum rate of flow (m^3/s)
V = maximum velocity through screen (m/s)
D = depth of flow at screen at maximum flow (m)

To prevent deposition of grit in the screening chamber the velocity of the sewage in the approach channel should not fall below 0.5 m/s; and to prevent screenings being washed through the screen the velocity at the screen at maximum flow should not exceed 0.9 m/s.

3.4 Small Sewage Works

There are about 6500 sewage works in England and Wales, and 90 per cent of these serve populations of less than 10 000 and are mainly operated by mobile teams. Most of those built before 1980 were scaled-down large works with a disproportionate manpower requirement. In the decade to 1990 there was a major reduction in manpower throughout the industry, and the design of small works particularly, began to include package units for preliminary treatment incorporating automation and telemetry equipment.

Older types of coarse bar screens are still in use at some very small unmanned works. These are inclined bars set at an angle in the inlet channel with spaces of 50 to 75 mm. The operator stands on a platform above the channel and rakes the debris up into a perforated trough to drain and then to a wheelbarrow for disposal. Such screens are ineffective and block quickly, and have now been largely removed. However, many have been retained as stand-by screens when a screen or disintegrator has been built alongside. Ideally they should be situated upstream so that debris collected during a breakdown can be returned to the flow later.

Upward-flow screens are still common on small works because of their simplicity of operation. The screen bars are laid horizontally at the top of a chamber; sewage flows upwards through the screen and the debris which collects on the underside falls to the bottom of the chamber and is removed through a valve for drying and disposal.

3.5 Coarse Screens

Screens with apertures greater than 50 mm are sometimes installed at the inlet to a works or at a large pumping station. Their purpose is to protect the equipment from damage by large objects such as logs of wood. Such screens also accumulate debris that more properly should be removed downstream by the medium and fine screens. Mechanized cleaning has never been successful and if possible coarse screen installations are to avoided.

Rotating Bar Interceptors are not really screens in the accepted sense, but protect downstream equipment from larger objects, and are often installed at large pumping stations. They consist of vertical bars in the channel spaced at centres usually greater than 75 mm. Each bar driven by an hydraulic motor rotates clockwise and then anticlockwise with a peripheral velocity approximating the sewage flow thus presenting a moving surface to the sewage solids and assisting passage through. The rotation unwinds debris that accumulates. Larger objects are removed by hand.

3.6 Medium Screens

Screens in this category have spaces between the bars of 15 to 50 mm, but mostly in the range 15 to 25 mm. This has been the traditional size, and screens of this type have served the industry well. There is still a high demand for them and manufacturers include several varieties within their ranges.

The three main types of screen are the curved bar, vertical straight bar, and the inclined straight bar; each is available with a variety of raking mechanisms. Screen cleaning can be activated by differential level detectors or time controls. In most installations the rake operates on the front face of the screen receiving the sewage flow, but a preference is now being expressed for back-raked screens. In these, the debris cannot be forced forward through the screen by the rake, the mechanism is less likely to be jammed by large objects in the sewage, and the raking action is more positive especially at the bottom of the screen.

The curved bar screen is suitable for use where the channel is generally not more

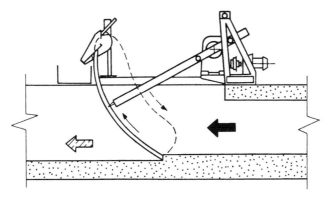

Fig. 4. Screen with semi-rotary rake

than 2.5 m below ground level; the motor driven rake follows the curvature of the screen maintaining contact between the bars. A tine-cleaning device is mounted on top of the channel and sweeps the screenings to a trough or belt. An example is shown in Fig 4.

The vertical bar screen is used for deeper channel applications, and the raking mechanism can be based on an endless chain or can be a reciprocating grab riding on a carriage and held clear of the screen on the downward travel. At the lowest

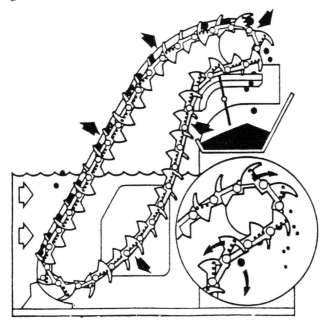

Fig. 5. Moving belt screen

point the teeth are forced between the bars and the rake returns to the top of the screen where a blade scrapes the debris onto a conveyor.

3.7 Fine and Milli-screens

Screens with spaces less than 15 mm and usually about 6 mm have become the standard for the 1990s. The volume of screenings produced is very much greater than with medium screens, and washing and dewatering equipment is specified to reduce the volume for disposal and its obnoxious nature.

This is an area of continuing development and an accepted nomenclature has not yet evolved. In this manual the different types available are referred to as: Moving Belt, Rotary, Static and Sac screens.

3.7.1 Moving belt screens. This category includes examples such as Aquaguard, Filterscreen, Filtaband and the Step Screen and there are many others. These types of screen operate as continuous, self cleansing, moving belts always presenting a clean face to the sewage flow. The apertures take the form of slots commonly 6 mm wide and 25 mm long. Sewage passes through the slots and debris retained on the screen is raised on the belt out of the flow. Then at the top of its travel, the debris is lifted off the screen by the relative movement of the segments of the screen

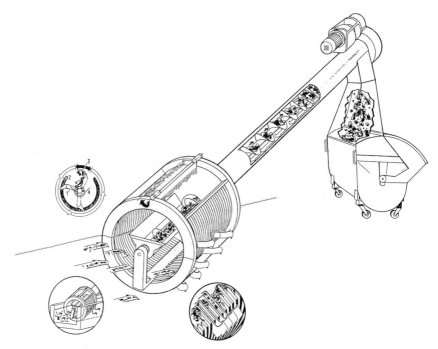

Fig. 6. Rotamat screen

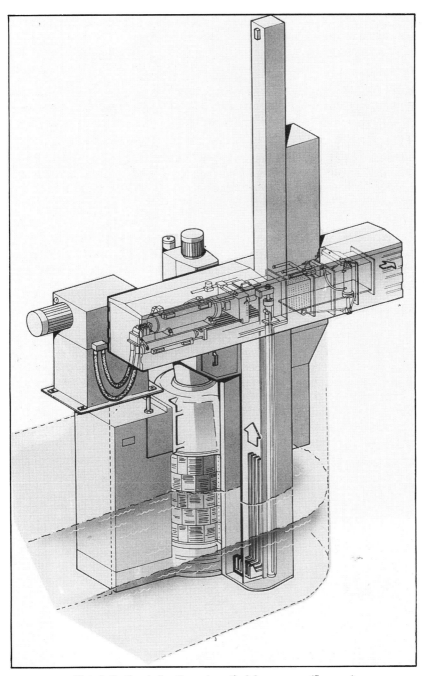

Plate 1. Sectional view through vertical drum screen (Screezer)

between one another, and it is removed either by a brush or by water jets (Fig. 5). The belt then returns to the channel to repeat the action. Debris can be discharged to a water trough, a dry conveyor, or directly into a dewatering device.

3.7.2 Rotary screens. The well-established cup and drum screens are included in this category as well as the newer devices such as the Vertical Drum Screen (Screezer), Rotamat and Contrashear. New variations are being introduced all the time and only a general description can be given.

These screens are all rotating drums immersed to varying degrees in the sewage flow. In most cases sewage enters one end of the drum and passes through slots or perforations leaving the debris on the inside to be removed by some form of scrolling device. Screenings are flushed from the screen by water jets directed onto the outer face. An example is shown in Fig. 6.

The Screezer (Plate 1) is a development from the Comminutor (see section 3.10). Simply, the face of the Comminutor has become the fine screen and the rotation of the screen drum moves the debris to one side from where it is lifted to the dewaterer at ground level. The Screezer can replace a Comminutor in the same formwork and is often specified for that reason.

The axis of a drum screen is across the direction of flow (Fig. 7). Sewage passes through the mesh, and the screenings collect on the outer face and are washed off on the downward side by the cascading action of the sewage carried up by the rising side of the drum. Drum and cup screens are reliable and effective, but hair-pinning or bridging between adjacent holes in the screen mesh has been a problem. Hair and fibre woven between the apertures can form a dense mat blinding the surface. The relationship between the thickness of the plate and the diameter of the aperture is critical, and in one installation when 2 mm gauge plate was replaced by 4 mm hairpinning ceased.

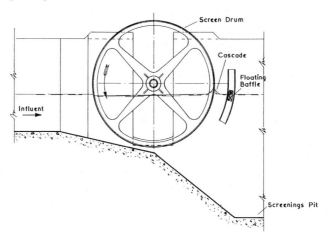

Fig. 7. Drum screen

A gauge of 9 mm is usually recommended with 5 mm apertures. Grease, which is more prevalent in holiday areas, has a tendency to accumulate, and more powerful washing and even steam cleaning may be necessary. A dewatering device is usually an integral part of the equipment.

3.7.3 Static screens. These are usually developments of the traditional medium screens but with narrower apertures, or the bars are replaced by perforated sheet and the rake by a brush. Examples include the 'D' Screen, Brush Screen, and the Fine Bar Screen. The recently introduced Disc Screen does not fit clearly into any category. It consists of vertical shafts each fitted with overlapping and intermeshing discs giving apertures betweem 2.5 and 5 mm. Each shaft rotates slightly faster than its upstream neighbour thereby conveying the debris across the face of the screen to the discharge point.

A Run-down Screen is an inclined plate of wedge wire or perforated material onto which sewage discharges and flows downwards. The liquid drains rapidly through the plate, the debris remaining on the upper surface and collecting at the bottom of the incline.

3.7.4 Sac screens. These are not normally specified as part of a preliminary treatment process, but are commonly installed immediately before biological filters and on final effluent outfalls. They intercept debris which has passed through the inlet works and the settlement tanks. Their principal benefit is to reduce the need to prick out the holes in the distributor arms. They are also used to prevent debris passing out of an activated sludge works which does not have an inlet works or settlement tanks.

They consist of loosely woven mesh sacks suspended over a weir, often in the dosing siphon chamber. The settled sewage flows into the sack and debris is held on the inside. The continual flow through the sack keeps the screenings clean. When the sack is full it is replaced, often twice a week, but the frequency is variable. Installations need to be considered carefully because sacks which are too heavy or in awkward situations can create hazardous working conditions for operators. Supporting frames and hoists are integral parts of larger installations to allow drainage and transfer to a platform for easier removal.

3.8 Screenings Dewatering

Screenings are objectionable because of the presence of faecal matter and sanitary items. Sewage solids which have been pumped and have travelled some distance in the sewerage system tend to be more broken down before they arrive at the sewage works and are less noticeable in the screenings. By contrast in short gravity systems larger amounts of faecal matter are removed by fine screens giving the dewatered screenings an objectionable appearance and odour.

Burial on site and carting to the local authority tip in the raw state is less accept-

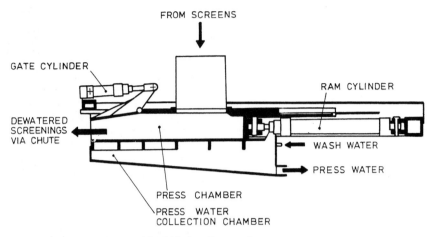

Fig. 8. Hydraulic screenings press

able today and there are now a large number of dewatering devices available to render screenings less offensive so that they can be disposed of by an environmentally acceptable method. The proposed method of final disposal will usually decide the type of dewatering equipment, depending on whether it is important for the screenings to be free of faecal matter, or to be much drier and compressed. Bagging units are often installed particularly at medium-sized works.

Most suppliers provide some form of washing to reduce the amount of faecal solids. It usually consists of high pressure jets directed onto the screenings, but this is sometimes limited by the hydraulic capacity of the equipment and, disappointingly, is rarely effective. The most successful method for washing out faecal matter is to disintegrate the screenings in one of the new generation of disintegrators now available. The dryness of the product depends on the type of dewaterer used, and the equipment is developing rapidly.

3.8.1 Hydraulic ram. The Passavant, the Launder Feed Press, and Hydropress are the well known examples of this class. Screenings are deposited in the washing/drainage zone where water jets break down and wash out faecal matter, and then the ram forces the debris into a compression chamber (Fig. 8 and Plate 2).

The back pressure can be created by an hydraulically operated valve opening at a predetermined pressure, though smaller versions often rely on an upward inclined discharge tube. Drainage occurs at the compression point and again as the plug moves along the discharge pipe. These units produce a product with 50 to 60% moisture.

3.8.2 Screw compactors. Debris from the screen falls onto the screw where water jets break down the faecal matter which is washed out through the drainage system. Some models incorporate a screw with a decreasing pitch which compresses the

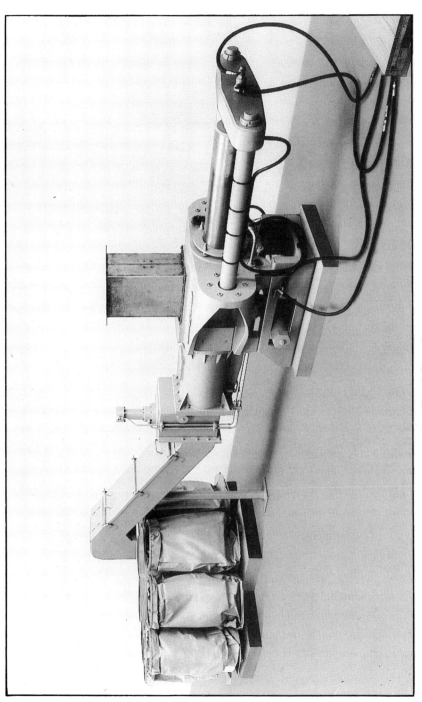

Plate 2. Screenings press

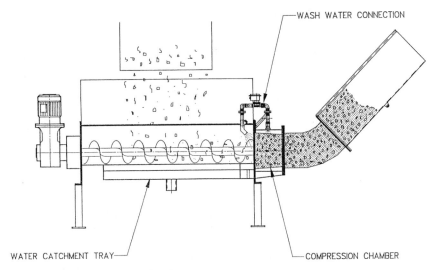

Fig. 9. Screw compactor

debris as it is conveyed. The screw conveys the screenings to the compaction zone where more drainage occurs before passing through the spring tensioned flap or up the inclined discharge chute (Fig. 9). This section often has pipework for drainage of liquors back to the inlet of the works. The dewatered screenings have a moisture content of 60%.

3.8.3 Parkwood Washer-Dewaterer. The Parkwood Washer-Dewaterer (Fig. 10) incorporates a disintegrator to positively break down and wash out the sewage solids. In the first stage of the process drainage water carries finely divided organic matter through a perforated screen, and the remaining fibrous and plastic matter

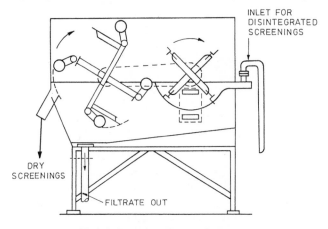

Fig. 10. Screenings Washer-Dewaterer

then passes to a second stage where it is squeezed against perforated sheet by rotating rollers. The final product with 60 to 65% moisture is clean and inoffensive.

3.8.4 Lisep process. The Lisep process separates the screenings and water by centrifugal action. Screenings are first disintegrated and pumped into a distribution chamber. From here they enter the bottom of an enclosed stainless steel conical screen which has 1.5 mm perforations. The screenings are thrown against the screen by the centrifugal action induced by a stainless steel paddle revolving at 1450 rpm, and are then worked up the screen by a scrolling action. The separated liquid drains through the perforated mesh and returns to the works inlet. The dry solid material is innocuous and aesthetically acceptable.

3.9 Screenings Incineration

Separate incineration at sewage works is not widespread but with the greater effectiveness of screenings dewaterers, it has become more practicable even though the calorific value is too low to maintain autothermic combustion. A cheap source of fuel such as digester gas or waste oil is essential. The process has been described by Pace and Price for the unit at Trowbridge[16], and by Newman for that at Stroud[17].

Dewatered screenings are fed into a combustion chamber lined with refractory materials and continuously agitated by rabble arms, the ash passing through slots in the grate. The exhaust gases pass through an afterburner to ensure complete oxidation of noxious gases. The temperature necessary for this is 800°C, and the fuel may be oil, natural or digester gas.

3.10 Disintegration

Disintegrators break up the solid matter in sewage or sludge into very small particles. They are widely used at sewage works for in-flow disintegration of the sewage, for side-flow disintegration of the screenings alone, and prior to sludge treatment and disposal. Smaller sewage pumping stations have disintegrators combined with a pump as a single unit to avoid blocking small diameter rising mains. At smaller sewage works disintegration may be used instead of screens obviating the need for separate removal and disposal.

Disintegrators have been available for many years but improvements in the technology and a wider appreciation of their potential has led to them being more widely used. The main types of disintegrator are illustrated by the Muncher, the C & H Macipump, the Mutrator and the Comminutor though the latter is no longer available.

The Muncher (Fig. 11 and Plate 3) is a low speed disintegrator consisting of two parallel vertical shafts fitted with intermeshing steel cutters contra-rotating at different speeds. It can be installed in channels, chambers or pipelines, and used in combination with centrifugal or positive displacement pumps. Solid material is nipped, crushed and torn as it passes through the cutters.

Plate 3. Muncher disintegrator

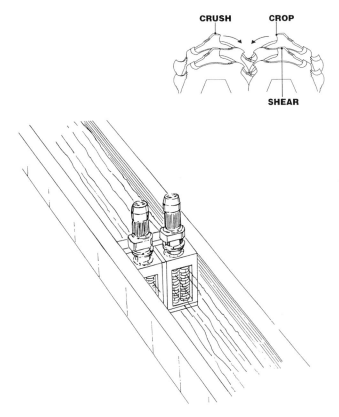

Fig. 11. Muncher disintegrator (inset, teeth)

The Macipump (Fig. 12) follows the more traditional pattern of disintegrator. It is a high speed centrifugal type pump which incorporates a rotating headstock with cutting edges running against a fixed hardened steel shear plate with 6 mm apertures. Sewage is drawn in through the bottom onto the shear plate and the rotating cutting edges of the headstock break the solid matter to a size that will pass through the apertures. The Macipump is often operated in combination with the Parkwood Washer-Dewaterer or the Lisep Separator described earlier.

The Mutrator is a positive displacement pump with a centrifugal type of disintegrator fitted in the suction line.

The Comminutor intercepts and macerates screenings without removing them from the flow. It consists of a cast-iron hollow drum rotating around a vertical axis. The hollow drum is a fine screen with horizontal slots, and fitted to the drum are projecting teeth which engage with a set of fixed hardened steel combs as the drum revolves. The debris retained on the screen is shredded between the teeth and combs, and this continues until the material passes through the slots. Comminutors

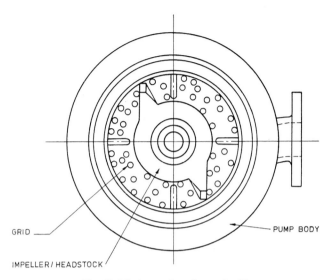

GRID

PUMP BODY

IMPELLER / HEADSTOCK

Fig. 12. Macipump impeller and grid

were very popular in the 60s and 70s, but maintenance became very expensive and they are no longer available. The Screezer (3.7.2) has been developed from it and fits into the same structure.

4. Grit Removal

4.1 Sources and Quantity of Grit

Grit may be defined as the heavy mineral material such as silt, sand, gravel or fragments of metal and glass present in sewage. It is abrasive and if not removed causes wear of pumps and other equipment, and blockages in tanks and pipes.

Since the density of grit is much greater than that of the other solids in the sewage there is a tendency for it to settle when the rate of flow is low. This may occur in a sewer with an inadequate gradient, in an inverted siphon or in a length of sewer which has subsided. There is also a tendency for grit to accumulate in the wet wells of pumping stations but this can be minimized by care in the design of the shape and capacity of the sump, pumping rates and frequency of pumping.

Grit which has been deposited in a sewer during the night when the flow is low may be flushed to the treatment works when the flow increases. Similarly grit which has accumulated in a sewerage system during periods of dry weather may be flushed to the treatment works in large quantities when storms occur. Even in sewers designed to maintain a self-cleansing velocity it is usual for the amount of grit in sewage to increase after rainfall of high intensity.

With a combined or partially-separate sewerage system, surface water entering the sewers from streets and paved areas is likely to contain large amounts of grit, especially during the early stages of a storm. Cracked or damaged sewers may allow ground water containing sandy material to enter. Grit from industrial effluents should be minimized by insistence on adequate pre-treatment at the factory.

At sewage works, grit may settle in pipes, channels and chambers resulting in blockages and uneven flow distribution. Large amounts can also accumulate in digesters, which then have to be taken out of service and emptied. Small sewage works do not usually have designated grit removal equipment, and the grit is allowed to settle in the settlement tank.

There is a very wide variation in the quantities of grit reported from different sewage works, mainly due to unrecorded deposits in screen chambers, channels and sedimentation tanks. The range is generally between 0.005 and 0.05 m^3 per 1000 m^3 of sewage. A higher range of 4 to 12 m^3 per 1000 persons per year was quoted in a paper[18] for the Standing Technical Committee of the National Water Council (NWC). Similarly the data for water and organic content show a wide

range of values and are unreliable. The absence of data suggests that grit disposal is
not a problem and records are not kept.

4.2 Theory of Grit Settlement

The equation for grit settlement is based on Stokes' Law and is as follows:

$$V = \frac{2gr^2}{9\eta} \times (D_s - D_l)$$

where V = settlement velocity of particle (m/s)
      D_s = density of particle (kg/m³)
      r = radius of particle (m)
      η = viscosity of liquid (kg/m.s)
      D_l = density of liquid (kg/m³)
      g = gravitational acceleration (m/s²)

In applying this formula to the settlement of grit, the important factor is the
difference in density between the particles of grit and the sewage in which they are
suspended. Since grit has a high density of about 2500 kg/m³, plant for removing it
is usually designed to reduce the velocity of the sewage so that grit settles but less
dense organic matter remains in suspension and is carried forward.

4.3 Detritus Tanks

Grit or detritus tanks at some of the older sewage treatment works were designed
and installed before the modern concept of grit removal was established. They are
settlement tanks or pits with somewhat arbitrary dimensions, and have a capacity
equivalent to one hundredth of the dry weather flow. Usually they remove most of
the grit and also a large proportion of the heavier organic matter.

Deposited material is removed manually, or by means of a mechanical grab.
Detritus tanks have been largely replaced by more efficient designs.

4.4 Constant Velocity Grit Channels

The principle used in settling grit from sewage and leaving the less dense organic
matter in suspension utilizes velocity control. The optimum velocity of sewage for
grit settlement is 0.3 m/s, and the problem is how to maintain this at all rates of
flow. The mathematical basis for design was worked out by Townend[19] who
demonstrated that if a flume was located immediately downstream of an open
channel to control the depth of flow, and if the cross sectional area of the channel at
any level could be made proportional to the rate of flow, a constant liquid velocity
would be maintained.

This is possible by making the channel of parabolic cross section. However, to
facilitate the removal of the grit and simplify construction, Townend departed
slightly from the theory and used a trapezoidal cross section. Channels designed on

this basis are called constant velocity grit channels, and sufficient channels are provided to enable them to deal with the maximum flow when all are in operation (Plate 4).

Moderate variations in the velocity above and below 0.3 m/s are permissible, but if the velocity falls outside the range 0.2–0.4 m/s, either organic matter will also be deposited or the finer grit will fail to settle.

The flow through each channel is regulated by a standing wave flume at the outlet which ensures that the velocity of flow is maintained at the design value over the range of flows received. The number of channels in use can be controlled by electrically operated penstocks actuated by a flow recorder on the measurement flumes.

When the velocity of flow is 0.3 m/s, most of the grit will settle and since grit particles fall vertically in sewage at about 0.03 m/s, the theoretical length of a grit channel is given by the formula:

$$\text{Length of channel} = \frac{\text{Depth of flow in channel} \times \text{velocity}}{0.03}$$

i.e. length = 10 × maximum depth of flow.

To compensate for turbulence and to allow for different sizes of grit particles with varying settling velocities, it is usual for the length of a grit channel to be about 20 times the maximum depth of flow.

On smaller works the removal of grit from the channels is usually carried out manually. On larger works grit removal is carried out by submersible pumps or a vacuum suction device mounted on a travelling gantry, or by a travelling dredger fitted with metal buckets. The grit is usually discharged to a settlement basin or cyclone type washer from which the organic material and transport water are removed prior to disposal.

4.5 Spiral-Flow Grit Channels

These are rectangular tanks through which sewage follows a spiral path. They are also known as aerated grit channels. At peak flow the retention time is about three minutes. The spiral flow is initiated by the incoming sewage entering tangentially at the base of the tank, and is maintained by the air lift effect of a row of diffusers mounted close to the opposite longitudinal wall. Grit settles and is carried into collecting hoppers below the air diffusers and is withdrawn through valves to classifers (Fig. 13 and Plate 5).

Adjustment of the amount of air introduced affects the velocity of flow in the settling zone close to the base of the channel; excessive air keeps fine grit in suspension, and too little allows organic matter to settle. This ability to vary the air supply allows the performance to be adjusted according to operational experience.

Plate 4. Constant velocity grit channels

Plate 5. Spiral-flow grit channel

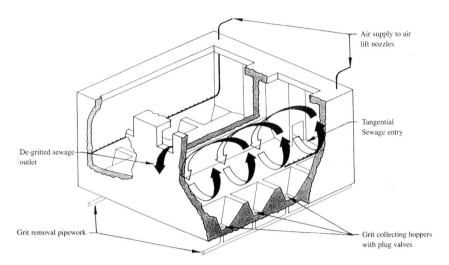

Fig. 13. Spiral-flow grit channel

It is important that grit is not allowed to consolidate in the hoppers, and should always be discharged into a pipeline of flowing water. Plug-type valves with a horizontal seating face perform better than side exits through penstocks, because the action of opening disturbs the grit which has settled above the valve. A flushing valve upstream allows sewage to be drawn into the grit pipeline before any of the valves are opened during the degritting cycle.

The valves are progressively opened and closed, emptying the individual hoppers in turn. Induced vortex centrifugal pumps with recessed impellers are suitable for pumping waterborne grit. There should be provision for backflushing the grit pipework with high pressure washwater, and for introducing compressed air into the hoppers to fluidize consolidated grit. The entire process can be automated.

4.6 Cross-Flow Detritor

A Detritor consists of a square tank of shallow depth with the inlet channel angled to the direction of flow across the unit (Fig. 14).The angle at which the approach channel is constructed in relation to the tank is given by the formula:

$$\sin \theta = \frac{W_c}{W_d}$$

where θ = angle between approach channel and tank
  W_c = width of approach channel (m)
  W_d = width of entry to detritor (m)

A series of vertical concrete deflector baffles, pivoted at the top and bottom and fitted across the full width of the tank at the inlet, are adjusted and then fixed to

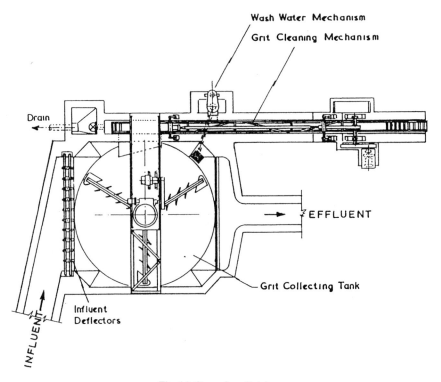

Fig. 14. Cross-flow Detritor

achieve an even distribution of flow across the unit. If the baffles are incorrectly set, short circuiting occurs and grit settlement will be less effective. A weir at the outlet of the tank retains the grit on the flat bottom.

The radial scraping mechanism is carried on supports spanning the tank. Settled grit is removed continuously from the centre to the periphery, where it is pushed into a sump which forms the base of a ramped channel. Grit is moved up the ramp by a reciprocating rake to discharge into a skip or trailer. An impeller induces a counterflow of sewage between the base of the inclined rake and the tank to separate and carry away the organic matter. Alternatively the grit may be pumped to a separate free-standing classifier.

The Detritor may be operated continuously at peak flow, but under normal flow conditions it is operated for about 20 minutes at intervals of 2 to 4 hours and is controlled either by a time switch or flow actuator.

Where a Detritor has to be installed below ground level, such as in a deep sewer or ahead of a pumping station, the grit is often separated by a cyclonic classifier. This consists essentially of a cast iron, conically shaped unit into which the feed from the grit pump enters tangentially, developing a vortex. Centrifugal forces throw the grit to the walls of the conical section, and as the grit collects in the apex it is discharged through a valve.

4.7 Vortex-Type Grit Separators

A vortex grit separator consists of a circular tank which sewage enters tangentially creating a vortex. Separated grit is deposited in the bottom, and organic matter in the sewage overflows for further treatment.

The Jeta (formerly the Pista) grit trap (Fig. 15) employs the vortex principle and is designed so that paddles and peripheral drag maintain the correct horizontal velocity of the sewage while flowing through a circular tank. Sewage enters tangentially, flows around the tank and leaves parallel to the inlet. Grit settles in the quiescent outer zone of the tank and falls onto the inclined floor, and thence into the lower collection hopper. The impeller is situated between the upper and lower chambers, and designed to produce a radial force to allow the grit to settle, and an upward spiral flow around the centre encouraging the lighter solids to rise. Grit is removed from the lower chamber by an air lift pump, and may then be washed and dried prior to disposal.

The Grit King Separator (Fig. 16) consists of a cylindrical vessel with a sloping base and a top assembly of a shaft, cone and dip plate. Sewage enters tangentially

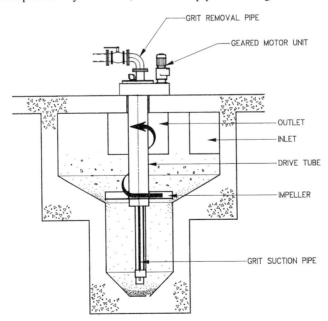

Fig. 15. Jeta grit trap

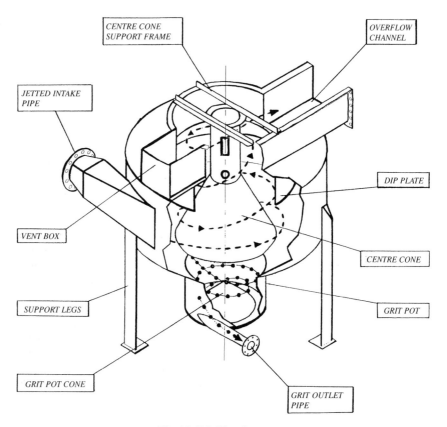

CENTRE CONE
SUPPORT FRAME

OVERFLOW
CHANNEL

JETTED INTAKE
PIPE

DIP PLATE

VENT BOX

CENTRE CONE

SUPPORT LEGS

GRIT POT

GRIT POT CONE

GRIT OUTLET
PIPE

Fig. 16. Grit King Separator

and rotates around the perimeter allowing grit to settle. This process is aided by the drag forces at the boundary layer on the wall and bottom surfaces of the vessel. The main flow is directed upwards towards the middle of the vessel as a narrower spiralling column rotating at a lower velocity than the outer downward flow. This difference in velocity creates a shear zone which enhances the separation of lighter solids. The heavier grit collects in the pot in the base, and the main flow overflows at the top of the tank.

4.8 Disposal of Grit

Much of the plant supplied to remove grit from sewage incorporates washing or classifying equipment to remove excess organic matter, and loose water is usually removed by simple drainage.

The organic content of grit varies between 10 and 30% according to whether it has been washed. Even when grit washing is effective, the organic content may be 15%. Washed grit may be used for site roads or disposed of by burial.

5. Storm Sewage

5.1 Introduction

The quality of water flowing in a watercourse usually deteriorates following wet weather because of disturbance of the bottom layers, and the discharge of untreated storm sewage from overflows on sewerage systems. Reports to the Technical Committee on Storm Overflows and the Disposal of Storm Sewage[20] indicated that overflows set at 6 to 9 DWF were generally satisfactory for sewage flows up to 45 Ml/d when the stream flow exceeds 45 Ml/d, but, when the sewage and the stream flow were both small a 6 to 9 DWF overflow had only an even chance of being satisfactory. With increasing urban development, the proportion of impervious surface in an area served by a sewerage system increases, and runoff from roads and car parks to surface water sewers can be highly polluting.

The three types of sewerage system are: (a) the combined system where foul sewage and surface water are carried by the same sewer; (b) the partially-separate system in which surface water from the roads and fronts of properties is carried in a surface water sewer to the nearest suitable watercourse, and foul sewage, plus some surface water from roofs and yards, is taken to the sewage treatment works; and (c) the separate system where foul sewage and surface water are carried by separate sewers, one to the sewage works and the other to the nearest suitable watercourse. Storm sewage overflows are provided on combined and partially-separate systems.

5.2 Dry Weather Flow

The traditional practice of setting storm overflows at 6 DWF evolved during the late 19th century. Under the Rivers (Prevention of Pollution) Act 1951, it became necessary to obtain the consent of the River Board before making any new discharges or altering existing discharges to streams. Frequently a Board would stipulate a storm overflow weir setting equivalent to 6 DWF, and some 8 DWF, or even 10 DWF. There was no uniformity of practice and there were differences in interpreting what was meant by 6 DWF.

The dry weather flow is currently defined[21] as: "the average daily flow to the treatment works during seven consecutive days without rain following seven days during which the rainfall did not exceed 0.25 mm on any one day".

This definition is for sewage which is mainly domestic in character, and where there is a significant proportion of industrial effluent it should be based on the flow on five working days. In 1979 the DoE/NWC Technical Working Group on Waste Water Treatment[22] recommended that the DWF should be replaced by the median flow in dry weather. For a selected period (usually a quarter year) the median value is determined for all days on which the rainfall was less than or equal to 1.00 mm. The median flow is that value which when selected from a given number of all the eligible flows ranked in order of magnitude, forms the midpoint of the series. There is no evidence that this recommendation has been adopted by the industry.

5.3 Formula A

The Technical Committee on Storm Overflows and the Disposal of Storm Sewage was appointed in 1955, and their Final Report[20] was published in 1970. This, together with the Report on Storm Sewage: Separation and Disposal, published in 1977[23] by the Scottish Development Department, formed a comprehensive review of available knowledge. Both the Technical Committee and the Scottish Working Party found that there was insufficient working knowledge on which to base recommendations and both commissioned surveys and practical investigations.

The Technical Committee considered that there were too many storm sewage overflows, and that about 37 per cent of these were unsatisfactory. The main reason for the unsatisfactory overflows was that the weir settings were less than 6 DWF. If the traditional 6 DWF standard had been applied there would have been less of a problem.

The Technical Committee considered that the setting of a storm overflow should take into account the domestic water usage, infiltration, industrial effluent and storm sewage. Any formula must be acceptable to the users, simple to apply and be seen to represent a modest improvement. After considering three possible formulae the Committee finally recommended the following Formula A:

Storm overflow setting $= (PG + I + E) + 1.36P + 2E$ m^3 per day

where P = population
       G = average domestic water consumption (m^3/hd d)
       I = infiltration (m^3/d)
       E = the industrial effluent (m^3/d)

The Technical Committee recommended that the formula should be used in all situations and that only in special circumstances should any variation be made. The former terms '6 DWF' and '3 DWF' are still used in conversation, but users should note that the 'Full Treatment Flow' in particular may be significantly different from 3 DWF.

The DWF is represented in the formula by $(PG + I + E)$. Before an overflow operates the domestic sewage should be diluted by a further 1.36 m^3 per person and the industrial effluent by a further two volumes of surface water. The value of

1.36 m³ is the equivalent of the Technical Committee's figure of 300 gallons, which they adopted as an appropriate increase over five times the estimated average domestic sewage flow of 30 to 40 gallons per person per day, allowing for long term increases in water consumption.

Industrial effluent is often much more polluting than domestic sewage, and in wet weather the concentration of pollution from the overflow could increase and in some cases be greatly increased. The Technical Committee agreed that the overflow setting should be increased to minimize pollution, but with the great variety of industrial effluents and the lack of any helpful evidence it decided that it would be satisfactory to make provision for two extra volumes of rainwater for every one of industrial effluent.

5.4 Scottish Working Party Report

The Scottish Working Party[23] dealt with storm sewage tanks in use on sewerage systems. The majority of these were in operation at overflow settings greater than 6 DWF. They usually had retention periods of 6 hours at DWF, and in general were satisfactory.

The main advantage was the reduction in the frequency of discharge, and in the delay of discharges to the watercourse. When discharges to a stream needed to be of a higher standard than could be achieved by Formula A settings, storm tanks on the sewerage system could be justified. Investigations indicated that such storm tanks should have a capacity of 40 l/hd.

5.5 Flow to Full Treatment

In wet weather the maximum rate of flow to biological treatment has usually been expressed in multiples of DWF. The traditional setting was 3 DWF but to be compatible with Formula A, the Technical Committee recommended that the maximum rate of flow to receive biological treatment should be:

$$\text{Flow to full treatment} = 3PG + I + 3E$$

where P = population served
G = average domestic water consumption (m³/hd d)
I = infiltration (m³/d)
E = industrial effluent discharged in 24 hours (m³/d)

5.6 Separation of Storm Sewage

Sewage treatment works are not normally designed to provide biological treatment for all the storm sewage arriving in wet weather, and provision is made for storing flows in excess of the treatment capacity. Storm sewage is apportioned between that receiving biological treatment, and that being settled and stored for treatment later.

The usual point of separation is downstream of the preliminary treatment plant so that screenings and grit are removed.

The device used for separating storm sewage should:

a) not come into operation until the full treatment flow is passing forward to primary sedimentation and biological treatment;
b) be so designed that the flow to biological treatment remains constant at 3PG + I + 3E as the rate of flow of storm sewage to the works increases; and
c) be self cleansing, and so arranged that the maximum amount of polluting matter passes forward to primary sedimentation and biological treatment.

The usual method of separation is by a weir on one or both sides of the sewage channel. The rate of flow of sewage passing forward can be controlled by an electrically operated penstock downstream linked to a flow recorder. The flow rate should remain constant irrespective of the rate of flow of storm sewage arriving at the works. Other devices include a hydrobrake flow restriction, multiple trough overflows, float-operated regulating valves, and siphons. Where the sewage is pumped, separation may take place at the pumping station.

5.7 Treatment of Storm Sewage

5.7.1 Factors influencing the degree of treatment. Storm sewage is settled to remove suspended solids. Biological treatment is not usually considered necessary because the benefit to the watercourse in storm conditions would be low, and the cost of providing treatment capacity very high for the relatively few occasions it would be used.

The first flush of storm sewage arriving at a works is grossly polluting and it is the practice that the first storm tank does not have an outlet to the watercourse, and the contents of that tank are returned to the sewage inlet after the storm.

In some cases it may be necessary to treat the effluent from the storm tank to a higher standard, for example by irrigation over land. Such cases could include: (a) little dilution in the receiving watercourse, (b) the velocity in the watercourse is low, (c) the discharge is immediately upstream of a high amenity area, (d) the watercourse is a fishery, or (e) water is abstracted downstream for potable use.

5.7.2 Storm sewage tanks. Storm sewage tanks have two functions: to store as much of the storm sewage as possible for return to full treatment later, and to remove suspended solids with their associated BOD. The tanks are in use for less than 5 per cent of their life, and hence are sometimes used to give additional settlement to final effluents. They can also be used in emergency for temporarily storing sewage contaminated with an industrial effluent, or for receiving the flow of sewage during alterations or repairs.

There are normally two or more tanks with the first not having an outlet. The levels of the sills of the inlet weirs are designed so that the tanks fill in series. When the last tank has filled, the sills of the outlet weirs, which are all at the same level, but higher than the inlet weirs, permit the tanks to discharge in parallel. The first tank which has no outlet stores the first flush of strong storm sewage until the flow has returned to normal, when the contents are returned for full treatment.

The design of storm sewage tanks is often similar to that of primary sedimentation tanks but, as they have to provide efficient settlement at higher rates of flow particular attention should be given to baffling at the inlet to avoid short circuiting. The design should be such as to facilitate emptying the tanks and removing the sludge as soon as possible. If sludge is retained on the floor of the tank it dries out and is difficult to remove. Rectangular tanks are more popular, and are often fitted with cable-hauled sludge scrapers on rails in the bottom of the tank.

It is important that storm sewage tanks are emptied completely each time they are used, so that the storage capacity is available for the next rainfall. The whole of the contents of the tanks may be returned to the sewage flow upstream of the primary settlement tanks. The tanks can be designed so that the supernatant water can be returned for treatment and the sludge dealt with separately.

It has been common practice at treatment plants serving less than 10 000 persons to give biological treatment to the whole of the flow in wet weather, up to a maximum of Formula A. By eliminating the overflow weirs and storm tanks the design of the works is simplified and the work of the mobile gang is reduced. Since the storage function of storm tanks is lost the treatment plant and equipment must be designed for a wider range of flows.

5.7.3 Requirements for storm sewage discharges. The consent of the National Rivers Authority (NRA) is necessary for the discharge of an effluent from storm sewage tanks. The new legislation following privatization of the water industry carried forward the provisions of earlier legislation. Part III of the Water Resources Act, 1991 largely supersedes Part 2 of the earlier Control of Pollution Act, 1974 and Part III of the Water Act, 1989.

Under s.38 (1) and Schedule 10 of the new Act an application has to be made to the NRA and a Notice of this application may then be advertised before it is decided whether to give or to refuse a consent. Under s.189 it is the duty of the NRA to maintain registers containing details of the applications made, the consents given and the samples of effluents taken by the authorities.

The consents imposed on discharges of storm sewage are always related to the use and the location of the watercourses and to any industrial effluents which may be present. In the UK the effluent from storm sewage tanks may often have a consent standard of 150 mg/l suspended solids, and other chemical parameters (eg. Red List substances) as circumstances demand.

6. Flow Measurement

6.1 Introduction

For effective management of a sewage works, it is important to know the volume of sewage handled and the diurnal and seasonal variations. In addition the NRA can require measurement facilities at discharge points from sewage works.

In order to compare the efficiency of performance and the unit costs of different sewage works, reliable flow measurements are necessary at several stages of treatment. Operational control of the treatment processes now requires remote, automatic adjustments to be made between balancing tanks, storm tanks and full treatment flow, and also between processes, using weirs and automatic penstocks. Action is usually initiated by the flow measurement device or level detector, which can also activate automatic sewage samplers.

The population served, water use, diurnal and seasonal variations, and infiltration are all reflected in records of inlet flow measurements used to predict future trends and plan extensions. River monitoring and control, and the management of water resources are assisted by reliable long-term records of flow measurements and associated sampling programmes.

Rapid advances are being made in instrument technology to meet the demand for more specific, reliable and accurate flow information. However, conditions vary considerably at sewage works, and sewage arriving may have foam on the surface, suspended and emulsified grease, and a variable solids content. The flow pattern is irregular, conditions are often turbulent, and many different configurations of channels and pipes are in use.

Accurate and reliable liquid flow data can be obtained by direct measurement, given care in the choice of device, siting, installation and maintenance. Even so, errors of ± 20 per cent are common, although in recent years there has been a much greater awareness of the need to obtain credible data, and greater attention has been given to accurate measurement.

Since the mid-1970s air-reaction and float-operated devices have been almost completely superseded. Modern equipment makes use of electronic linearization of signals, and can be programmed to perform flow calculations for any measurement structure to BS 3680. It incorporates solid state memory capable of being downloaded to IBM compatible computers for readout available in several formats. Telemetry and digital-analogue converters permit the results to be displayed remotely, and alarm relays and flow-proportional output are available. Appropriate hydraulic structures should always be provided at smaller works for portable instruments.

It is not the intention in this chapter to deal exhaustively with the subject, which is well covered in several standard text books and publications[24,25,26] of the British Standards Institution.

The rate at which sewage arrives at a sewage treatment works varies diurnally in a manner unique to the particular sewerage network. Fig. 17 represents a typical pattern of flow on a dry day from a gravity sewerage system, but the presence of pumping stations within a system can influence the pattern considerably, and a widespread sewerage system could have a more uniform curve.

Most measurement sites are compromise choices and it is often necessary to make allowances for inherent inaccuracies which in total can be significant. Some of these inaccuracies may be attributable to the instrument or hydraulic structure, and can be minimized by regular maintenance and calibration of the instrument.

Other inaccuracies may be due to flows which bypass the meter or are added downstream, such as rainfall runoff and foul drainage within the site. Some flows may be 'double-counted' such as returns from primary settlement, humus tanks, storm tanks, recirculation, humus sludge, backwash liquors and decanted sludge liquors. An assessment of any misleading information must be made and if it is significant (perhaps greater than ±5% of the true flow) adjustments should be made.

6.2 Measurement Sites

Flow measurements can be made at many locations and the most commonly used are shown diagrammatically in Fig. 18. It will be noted in the example that while

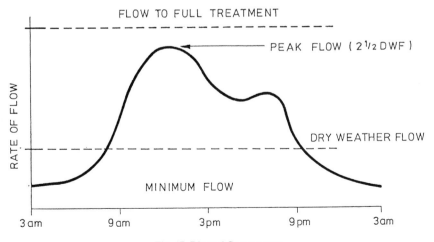

Fig. 17. Diurnal flow pattern

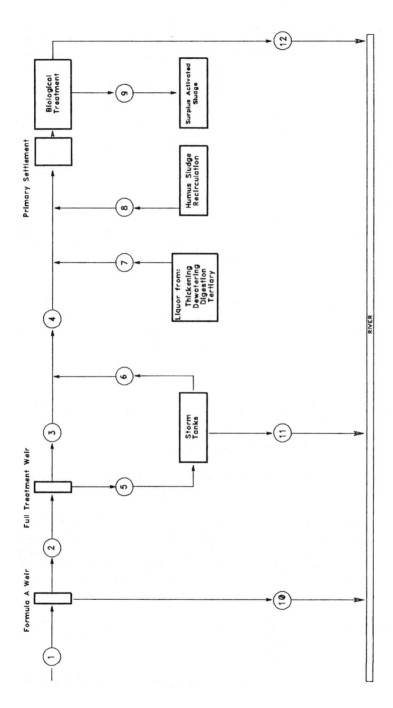

Fig. 18. Flow measurement sites

1 Total flow
2 Flow to inlet works
3 Flow to full treatment

4 Flow to full treatment
5 Flow to storm tanks
6 Return from storm tank

7 Sludge treatment liquors
8 Treatment return liquors
9 Surplus activated sludge

10 Untreated storm sewage
11 Settled storm sewage
12 Final effluent to river

there is only one inflow there are three possible outlets from the works; and some of the measurements can be deduced from combinations of readings. Additional flow meters may be needed at several other locations, e.g. effluent recirculation and return activated sludge lines. The value and comparability of the data obtained for each works will vary according to the location of the measurement sites.

Although flows should ideally be measured at several locations on a sewage treatment works, design constraints usually limit the possibilities, and generally where open channel measurement is adopted the position chosen is near the inlet. The site should be chosen to permit the measurement of flow passing forward to full treatment before return liquors from the site are added. These should be measured separately.

At small works a rectangular or a V-notch weir may be suitable because it is accurate at low flows and can accommodate a wide range of flow rates. In this instance the final effluent channel is a favoured site for measurement because it is less likely to be subject to obstruction and accumulations of solid matter such as could occur in an inlet channel. At sites where flooding from the watercourse occurs precautions may be necessary to avoid inaccurate measurements.

At larger works it will normally be necessary to measure the flow at several points, but the minimum requirement would be to measure: (a) flow to full treatment, (b) flow to storm tanks, (c) the flow in excess of Formula A passing without treatment to the watercourse, and (d) liquors passing between treatment processes.

The location of sites for both permanent and periodic use should be considered at the design stage with reference to the guides of the British Standards Institution. At very small works a measurement point should be provided which gives flow characteristics suitable for measurement by portable equipment.

6.3 Measurement Structures

Structures in common use for flow measurement at sewage works include the standing wave flume, rectangular or V-notch weirs, and the venturi flume.

6.3.1 Standing wave flume. A flume is a specially shaped open channel providing a restriction which results in an increase in velocity and a change in level of the liquid flowing through it. It has a converging section to restrict the flow, a throat and a diverging section, and there must be sufficient length of straight channel upstream and downstream to ensure local stability. The ideal characteristics are defined in BS 3680[24], and prefabricated units are available for most applications.

The standing wave flume (Fig. 19) is sometimes known as the critical depth or free discharging flume, terms which describe its main characteristics, in contrast to the venturi flume which is not related.

The standing wave flume must have a free discharge throughout the measure-

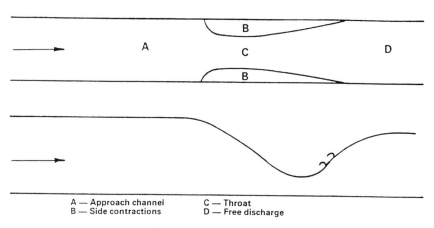

A — Approach channel   C — Throat
B — Side contractions   D — Free discharge

Fig. 19. Standing wave flume

ment range, and the velocity in the approach channel must be less than the critical velocity. If the velocity of approach is greater than the critical velocity, the readings will be low, and if there is no free discharge downstream the flume is said to be drowned, and the reading will be high. Downstream the velocity is supercritical and a hydraulic jump or standing wave is formed.

There is a unique relationship between the depth in the throat at the critical velocity and the depth in the approach channel, so that it is only necessary to measure the head in the approach channel. The relationship between head and discharge is complex, and British Standard 3680 should be referred to. For a standing wave flume the discharge Q (m³/s) is given approximately by:

$$Q = 1.71 \ BH^{1.5}$$

where B is the width of the throat of the flume (m), and H is the head in the approach channel over the invert of the throat in the flume (m).

In the past, the head was measured by float-operated or air-reaction types of sensor situated in a stilling chamber alongside the approach channel. Measurement requires the liquid level to be converted to a flow rate based upon the discharge formula, and a device to linearize the output has to be incorporated. Formerly, linearization was achieved by mechanical means but is now carried out by electronic devices.

Flumes can deal with a wide range of flow and there is only a small loss of head with 70 to 80% of the initial head being recovered. They are self-cleansing and the liquid level is determined accurately, and is easily verified.

6.3.2 Venturi flume. This is not related to the standing wave flume but has often been confused with it because of their similar plan views. It operates on the same principle as the venturi meter in pipes and does not form a standing wave. It is therefore necessary to measure the head in the approach channel and also at the throat of the flume. The discharge Q (m³/s) is related to the difference between the two levels by the approximate general equation:

$$Q = 0.3 \; Bh \times \sqrt{210 \, (H - h)}$$

where: H is the depth over invert in the approach channel (m)
        h is the depth over invert in the throat (m)
        B is the width of the throat of the flume (m)

6.3.3 Thin plate weirs. A flow-measuring weir is an obstruction which is placed across a channel with an opening or notch of precisely defined shape and size through which the liquid flows. The thin plate weir (sometimes called the sharp-crested weir) comprises a vertical metal plate, set at right angles to the flow. The top edge is chamfered on the downstream side of the weir plate to enable the liquid (nappe) to spring clear, and the weir plate must be flush with the upstream face of the support.

The rate of flow over a thin plate weir depends on the head over the weir and the size and shape of the discharge area. Weirs have disadvantages compared to flumes that they incur a greater loss of head, and solids may accumulate behind the weir plate or on the weir edge, reducing the accuracy of the measurement. However, their ease of installation and low cost are considerable advantages. Triangular and rectangular weirs are the most common, but compound, trapezoidal, proportional and linear weirs are also used.

Complete discharge tables covering a wide range of flows for both V-notch and rectangular weirs (contracted or suppressed) are available but where practicable weirs should be calibrated at the site. Newer electronic flow recorders can be programmed for any configuration.

a) **Triangular or V-Notch Weirs**
This is the most accurate type of weir, with an error of $\pm 1\%$ of the true flow over a range of head of 0.05–0.35 m. The discharge formula for angles between 20° and 100° is:

$$Q = C_d \; \frac{8}{15} \; \tan \frac{a}{2} \; \sqrt{2g} \; H^{2.5}$$

where Q is the rate of flow (m³/s)
      C_d is the coefficient of discharge (dimensionless, and usually 0.6)
      a is the angle of the notch
      g is the acceleration due to gravity (m/s²)
      H is the measured head (m)

For a 90° V-notch, which is the most commonly used, the formula reduces approximately to:

$$Q = 1.42 \; H^{2.5}$$

and, for very low flows, notch angles of 53° 8′ ($Q = 0.71 \; H^{2.5}$) or 28° 4′ ($Q = 0.34 \; H^{2.5}$) are sometimes used.

b) **Rectangular Weirs**

Rectangular thin plate weirs (Fig. 20) are more applicable to larger flows than V-notch weirs.

i) Contracted weirs are those in which the rectangular opening in the weir plate is narrower than the width of the channel in which it is set. The accuracy of a contracted weir is normally within ±2% of the true flow.

ii) Suppressed weirs are those in which the weir extends across the full width of the channel so that the sides of the channel also serve as the side of the weir. With this type it is essential to provide air vents to ventilate below the nappe, allowing the liquid to overflow without contacting the downstream side of the weir. Suppressed weirs are more suitable for very large flows.

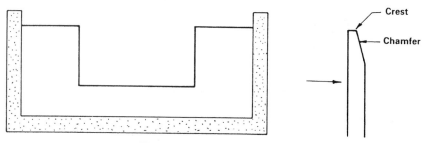

Fig. 20. Rectangular notch weir

The discharge formula for rectangular weirs may be expressed as:

$$Q = C_d \, \frac{2}{3} \, \sqrt{2g} \, BH^{1.5}$$

where Q is the rate of flow (m³/s)

C_d is the coefficient of discharge (dimensionless and close to 0.6)

g is the acceleration due to gravity (m/s²)

B is the effective width of the weir (m)

H is the measured head (m)

6.4 Measurement Devices

The rate of flow passing a fixed point in an open channel is the product of the average velocity at that point and the cross sectional area of the liquid flow. In an open channel the cross sectional area will vary with the head of flow upstream, and the rate of flow may be determined by applying the appropriate formula.

In pipes running full the cross sectional area is constant and the velocity may be determined by using pressure differential, magnetic flux or ultrasonic devices such as used in venturi, electromagnetic or Doppler type flow meters.

There are four main types of sensor: mechanical, electrical, acoustic and hydraulic and they may be used in open channels or pipes. The ones most commonly used in sewage treatment are as follows:

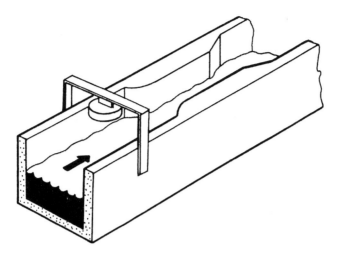

Fig. 21. Ultrasonic head over channel

Open Channel	**Closed Conduit**
Ultrasonic	Electromagnetic
Pressure transducer	Doppler
Air-reaction	Time of flight
Float	Venturi
Dipping probe	Orifice plate
Staff	
Hook gauge	

The analogue output from the sensor is used to drive indicators, chart recorders and integrators, and can be stored electronically for subsequent retrieval and processing.

In open channels, ultrasonic devices are mostly used because there is no contact with the sewage; and in closed conduits electromagnetic and ultrasonic sensors have now superseded other methods because they are more reliable and accurate, and require less maintenance than other devices.

6.4.1 Ultrasonic level device. This system (Fig. 21) has replaced the float and air-reaction systems for measurement of depth in association with flumes and weirs. The ultrasonic energy emitted from a combined transmitter/receiver installed above the liquid level is reflected back from the surface. The time which elapses between transmission of the signal and reception of the echo is proportional to the distance travelled, and hence indicates the depth of flow in the channel. Since velocity of sound changes with temperature, it is essential to incorporate compensation for this effect.

6.4.2 Pressure transducer. Pressure transducers have become available quite recently, and consist of an instrument on the bottom of a channel measuring the pressure head of the liquid flowing above. The main component of the pressure transducer is the silicon diaphragm which compares the pressure of the liquid on one side with that of air pressure on the other. The differential pressure is detected in resistors, converted to voltage and depth, and from the configuration of the channel, to the velocity.

6.4.3 Electromagnetic flow meter. The electromagnetic flow meter (Fig. 22) is based on the principle that the voltage induced in a conductor (i.e. sewage) passing through a magnetic field is a function of the mean velocity and hence the rate of flow. The meter[25] consists of a length of pipe lined with an insulating material, which may be hard rubber, butyl or polyurethane, with two diametrically opposed electrodes set flush with the inner surface. The magnetic field coils are bonded onto the outer surface of the pipe section and energized by a pulsed d.c. field. A signal converter evaluates the voltage induced between the electrodes to give a reading directly in units of flow.

The main advantages of these meters are that they are accurate, with a linear output with respect to flow, and cause no restriction, so pressure loss is negligible. They may be fitted easily into existing pipelines, and because of the averaging effect of the weighted magnetic field, they can be used for fluids of a difficult nature without the need for long straight lengths of pipe.

6.4.4 Ultrasonic time of flight. When an ultrasonic beam is transmitted at an angle across a pipe running full, its time of flight is shorter travelling with the flow than when travelling against it. The difference in velocity of the two beams is propor-

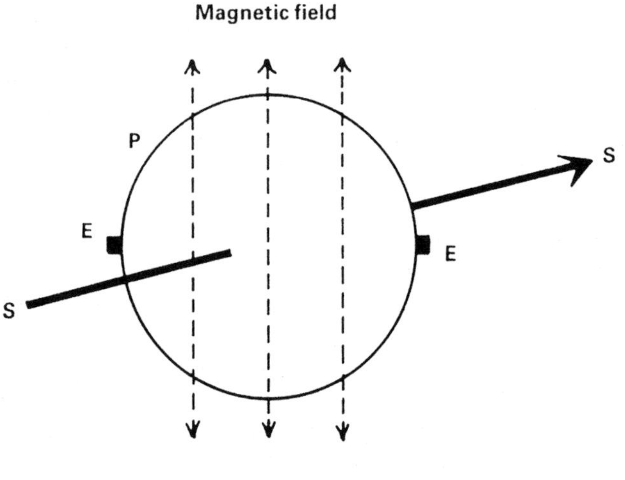

P — Insulated pipe,   S — Sewage flow,   E — Electrodes

Fig. 22. Electromagnetic flow meter

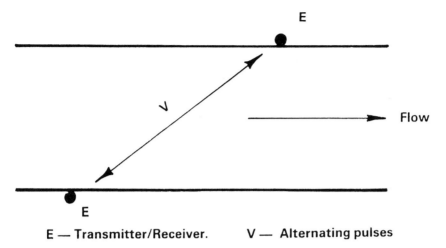

E — Transmitter/Receiver.   V — Alternating pulses

Fig. 23. Time of flight flow meter

tional to the mean rate of flow in the pipe. Two transmitter/receiver systems are situated diagonally on opposite sides of the pipe, and each transmits and receives pulses of sound alternately, so that the time of flight is determined in both directions (Fig. 23).

6.4.5 Ultrasonic Doppler meter. The Doppler phenomenon can be used to measure the velocity of a liquid in a pipe if the liquid contains particles of solids or air bubbles which reflect ultrasonic beams. Ultrasonic pulses of fixed frequency are transmitted through the cross-section of the pipe, and the movement of a solid particle or air bubble causes a shift in frequency. This shift between the transmitted and the reflected signal is proportional to the velocity of the particle, and hence of the liquid. The sensor head is bonded onto or into the pipe and consists of a transmitter projecting the ultrasonic beam at an angle of 60°. The signals reflected back are compared in the electronic circuit. This method has a lower accuracy than other devices.

6.4.6 Venturi meter. The venturi meter which is inserted into a pipeline consists of a short length of pipe tapering to a narrow throat and opening up downstream[26]. It is usually provided as a special flanged insert section for standard diameters of pipe.

The velocity of the sewage increases at the throat and the pressure falls, and as the pipe diverges the velocity falls and the pressure increases. The pressure is measured at the throat, and also upstream, by means of small diameter tubes inserted at several points around the pipe with ends flush with the internal diameter. The pressure difference between the two points is proportional to the square of the velocity, and hence the rate of flow may be calculated. The venturi meter is less commonly used for sewage because the small diameter tubes quickly block with sewage solids.

6.5 Calibration and Maintenance

There is often little choice in the siting of a flume or weir and even though it has been carefully manufactured and installed in accordance with the appropriate British Standard, it must be calibrated at regular intervals.

Access should be provided for checking the flume and channel for obstruction, and the datum peg. The sensor and the instrumentation associated with the flume or weir must be commissioned and calibrated carefully, and thereafter maintained in accordance with the manufacturer's instructions.

Records from some works have been found to have a margin of error exceeding $\pm 20\%$ arising from a combination of errors due to the instrument itself, errors in the channel and flume, and also to some of the flow being double counted or omitted completely. The accuracy of an instrument should be checked monthly against the calibration curve [depth (m), flow (m³/s)] for the flume or weir. For ultrasonic devices it is necessary to check that the base of the channel is zero. At a time of the day when the flow is reasonably constant and when sudden surges from pumps are unlikely, the depth of liquid should be accurately measured upstream of the flume, and converted to the rate of flow using the calibration curve.

The exercise should be repeated frequently during a period of perhaps 30 minutes, with time intervals arranged to coincide with convenient movements of the totalizer. At each measurement of depth the converted flow rate should be compared with that shown on the recorder chart.The various flow rates are averaged for the period of the test, and the volume of sewage which has passed the flume or weir during the test is determined and compared with the volume shown on the totalizer during the test.

At the time of commissioning and at appropriate intervals thereafter, a displacement test should be carried out. This consists of allowing an empty sedimentation tank to fill and taking a note of totalizer readings from the instrument at the beginning, at regular intervals, and at the end of the test, and comparing these with a succession of water level measurements taken from the side of the settlement tank. As an alternative to the displacement test, the salt dilution method using lithium chloride[27] or other suitable tracer may be used. Radioactive tracer techniques are very accurate but are subject to safety restrictions.

At older sites particularly, it is strongly advised that the channel is surveyed and the flume dimensions accurately measured to avoid errors due to changes since construction, such as ground settlement. At the time of commissioning of the sewage treatment works and at appropriate intervals, a detailed examination of the works flow diagram should be made to allow corrections to be made for omissions or double counts. Profiles of typical flows showing minimum night flows and weir overflow rates can be stored after calibration of the flume and meter. Subsequent data can then be compared with these records.

REFERENCES

1. CIRIA/WRc. Technical Note 119. Screenings and Grit in Sewage. Preliminary Report. CIRIA, London, 1984.
2. CIRIA/WRc. Technical Note 122. Screenings and Grit in Sewage. Phase 2, Further cost aspects of screening practice. CIRIA, London, 1985.
3. CIRIA/WRc. Technical Note 132. Screenings and Grit in Sewage. Phase 3, Storm water overflows and pumping stations. CIRIA, London, 1988.
4. BOON, A.G. Septicity in Sewers: causes, consequences and containment. *J.Instn. Wat. & Envir. Mangt.* 1992, **6,** (2), 79–90.
5. INSTITUTE OF WATER POLLUTION CONTROL. Proc. Symposium on Septic Sewage: problems and solutions. IWPC. May 1979.
6. NEWCOMBE, S., SKELLETT, C.F. AND BOON, A.G. An appraisal of the use of oxygen to treat sewage in a rising main. *Wat. Pollut. Control,* 1979, **78,** (4), 474–504.
7. TOOGOOD, S.T. Odour control for the 1990s—Hit or Miss?, *J. Instn. Wat. & Envir. Mangt.,* 1990, **4,** (3), 268–275.
8. CHAMBERS, B., WHITAKER, J. AND ELVIDGE, A. 'Waterbeach'—High quality effluent at small sewage treatment works. Symposium on Advanced Sewage Treatment, IWEM, November 1991.
9. EUROPEAN COMMUNITIES. Council Directive of 8th December 1975 concerning the quality of bathing waters. (76/160/EEC). *Official Journal of the European Community,* L31, 1976.
10. EUROPEAN COMMUNITIES. Council Directive of 4th May 1976 on pollution caused by certain dangerous substances discharged into the aquatic environment of the Community. (76/464/EEC). *Official Journal of the European Community,* L129, 1976.
11. HER MAJESTY'S INSPECTORATE OF POLLUTION. Letter to Managing Directors of Regional Water Authorities 'Guidance for Long Sea Outfalls—COPA Consent Applications'. HMIP 15th September 1988.
12. WATER RESEARCH CENTRE. Screening and grit removal at sewage treatment plants and sea outfall headworks. Proc. of Seminar, WRc, 9th December 1986.
13. WELSH WATER/WRc. *Users Guide, Preliminary Treatment for Marine Outfalls.* Joint Working Group on the Performance of Preliminary Treatment Facilities at Marine Outfalls, WRc, August 1989.
14. PAGE, S.J. Quantifying the screenings problem at sewage treatment works. *Wat. Pollut. Control,* 1986, **85,** (4), 420–426.
15. THOMAS, D.K., BROWN, S.J. AND HARRINGTON, D.W. Screening at marine outfall headworks. *J. Instn. Wat. & Envir. Mangt.,* 1989, **3,** (6), 533–547.
16. PACE, D.W. AND PRICE, D.J. A solution to screenings problems by dewatering and incineration. *Wat. Pollut. Control,* 1982, **81,** (3), 358–371.
17. NEWMAN, G.D. Operational experiences with a screenings washer-dewaterer, bagger and incinerator. *Wat. Pollut. Control,* 1986, **85,** (1), 57–62.
18. DoE/NWC. Standing Technical Committee on Waste Water Treatment, Report No. 13, February 1979.

19. TOWNEND, C.B. The elimination of the detritus dump. *J. Proc. Inst. Sew. Purif.*, 1937, (2), 58.

20. MINISTRY OF HOUSING AND LOCAL GOVERNMENT. Technical Committee on Storm Overflows and the Disposal of Storm Sewage: Final Report 1970.

21. INSTITUTE OF WATER POLLUTION CONTROL. Manuals of British Practice in Water Pollution Control, Glossary of Terms, IWPC, 1972.

22. NATIONAL WATER COUNCIL. Bulletin 43. Supplement No. 117. Technical Working Group on Waste Water Treatment. Median Flow in Dry Weather. November 1979.

23. SCOTTISH DEVELOPMENT DEPARTMENT. Storm Sewage: Separation and Disposal. Report of the Working Party, 1977.

24. BRITISH STANDARDS INSTITUTION, BS3680: Methods of Measurement of Liquid Flow in Open Channels, Parts 1–10.
    In particular: 4A: 1981 Thin Plate Weirs; 4C: 1981 Flumes

25. BRITISH STANDARDS INSTITUTION, BS5792: Electromagnetic flow meters.

26. BRITISH STANDARDS INSTITUTION, BS1042: Methods of Measurement of Sewage Flow in Closed Conduits, Parts 1 to 3.

27. DEPT SCIENTIFIC AND INDUSTRIAL RESEARCH. Notes on Water Pollution No 19, DSIR, December 1962.

INDEX

(Italic page numbers denote figures or plates)